2.

A.1

Sir WILLIAM MACEWEN

MACEWEN OF GLASGOW

A RECOLLECTION OF THE CHIEF

BY

CHARLES DUGUID

M.A., M.B., CH.B., F.R.F.P.S. (GLAS.), F.R.A.C.S.

OLIVER AND BOYD
EDINBURGH: TWEEDDALE COURT
LONDON: 39A WELBECK STREET, W.1
1957

PRINTED AND PUBLISHED IN GREAT BRITAIN
BY OLIVER AND BOYD LTD., EDINBURGH

PREFACE

THE difficulty of publishing in Britain from Australia is considerable, but this was overcome by the very generous offer of Emeritus Professor Matthew J. Stewart to act for me with the publisher. I am deeply grateful to him for this kindness and for his helpful criticism and advice.

.   .   .   .

Before proofs were ready we were deeply grieved to learn of his passing on 7th November 1956, despite the warning in one of his last letters—"my outlook is not of the brightest, so don't dawdle"—sturdy and pawky to the end. A friendship of fifty years waits to be renewed.

SINCE the death of Sir William Macewen several men of my time have suggested that I should write a memoir of the Chief, as Sir William was known to his students. But until the Annual Meeting of the British Medical Association in Glasgow in 1954, at which I was one of three representative delegates from South Australia, I had not felt any definite urge to comply. At that meeting my mind hied back to two previous British Medical Association Annual Meetings held in Glasgow—in 1888 and 1922. It was at the former that Macewen's reputation as a surgeon of international fame became firmly established. His address " On the Surgery of the Brain and Spinal Cord " made a profound impression on his audience and his demonstration of cases in many branches of surgery aroused a quite unusual enthusiasm in surgical circles. He was then 40, with wards in the Royal Infirmary. At the 1922 meeting he was 74, Regius Professor of Surgery at Glasgow University, and senior surgeon to the Western Infirmary. On this occasion he was President of the Annual Meeting and " Brain Surgery " was the subject of his presidential address. In addition to carrying out the usual duties of President he was to be found early every morning in his operating theatre with an interested audience of surgeons and in the afternoons he gave a series of demonstrations. He was throughout a great figure at the gathering and acclaimed as such. In 1954, thirty years after his death, he is still fully recognised as surgeon and scientist, but the man himself seems hardly to be known at all and because of that I find he is frequently misjudged.

I think I knew the Chief. It was my privilege to be in close touch with him over many years as student, surgical dresser, junior and senior house-surgeon, and afterwards as University, hospital and private assistant. I was an occasional guest in his home in Glasgow and at his country house in Bute. In 1923, as Immediate Past President of the British Medical Association, he visited Australia to attend the first Australasian Medical Conference held under the auspices of the parent body and I attended him during the sessions. The week he spent in Adelaide, Sir William, with his youngest son Dr Willie Macewen, stayed in my home.

On my way to the Mayo Clinic in 1927 Dr J. A. C. Macewen, Sir William's eldest son, gave me his card, on which he had written: " Introducing an old house-surgeon and assistant of my father—and also one of his most valued friends ". And in 1954 Dr Hugh Macewen, standing on the high ground at Garrochty as we looked across the Firth of Clyde to Goatfell in Arran, remarked : " You knew my father better than any of his assistants now alive ; you should write something ".

What I write is my personal recollection of Macewen as man and as surgeon in the period I knew him, 1906-1924.

I have written previously on the Chief. In the February 1917 issue of the Medical Students' Society Review of the University of Adelaide I described in detail Macewen's method of teaching and it is inevitable there can be little change in what appears here on that subject. And in the *Medical Journal of Australia* of 19th April 1924 I contributed an obituary appreciation.

There is a point of family interest to which I must refer. William Macewen was the youngest of twelve children. His eldest brother Thomas went to sea at an early age and, although he never returned, it was known that he landed in Australia and had settled at Roma in Queensland. Miss Macewen, when I was home in 1954, asked me if I would try on my return to trace her uncle's descendants. Illness in 1955 delayed the search, but on 19th March 1956 I was stirred to get a letter from a great-grandson of Thomas Macewen. He wrote on behalf of his grandfather, Robert McEwan, aged 81, whose hand was too shaky to write.

Robert McEwan, through his grandson, states that his father, on arrival in Melbourne in 1853, joined in the goldrush of that time and eventually made his way to Queensland. He came to Roma in its early days, acquired an extensive farm and was first Mayor of the town. His eldest son he called after his youngest brother William. The two brothers corresponded regularly but Thomas died when 54. After a lapse of three generations the families are again in contact. Miss Macewen has since informed me that Sir William's eldest sister, Janet, also went to Australia and settled in Sydney and that some of her married grandchildren visited the Macewen family at Garrochty in 1955.

Those of us who studied under Macewen will remember him best as the clinician in the Western Infirmary—the teacher sitting on the high white stool in the spacious corridor between the male surgical and male accident wards. Who can fail to recall the erect posture, the slight shake of the head that released the pince-nez, the sharp flick of the papers in his hand, and the " Ah, but " when we strayed in our argument from the path of logical reasoning? And can any of us forget the scene—the patient on the barouche wheeled in from the ward, three students of different years seated on shorter white stools, the class of ninety on benches in front of and to the right of the Chief, with the house-surgeon, the sister and a nurse in the offing?

Macewen's method of teaching was by question and answer. The junior man was usually asked to look at the patient and to describe what he saw, the other two being appealed to in turn. No palpation was allowed until Sir William was satisfied that each had used his eyesight to the best advantage. The three in turn were then allowed to use the hand and each was asked what he had made out. After this the junior was looked to for a diagnosis, not necessarily in technical terms but in his own words.

The full diagnosis might only be possible from the senior of the three, but each man during the course of an hour's catechising was required to give the reasons for his answers. The aim of the clinic was to teach each student to think for himself and to enable him to realise why he came to the conclusions he reached. The anatomy, physiology and pathology of the case were entered into as fully as the differential diagnosis and treatment. It was not only to the man on the floor that the questions applied, but also to those on the benches, each of whom was expected to follow the case in his mind and be ready with an answer if appealed to. Quite often the class had to file past the patient and each student was asked to write his name and his diagnosis on a slip of paper which was handed in. These were sorted by the assistants and laid before the Chief, who then discussed them. The main class was enabled to follow the case by means of a mirror slung from the roof, the angle of inclination being alterable at will. No effort was spared to lead out the student's mind. A bookish knowledge of surgery was neither asked for nor desired. The third time I was on the floor I had begun reading a textbook on surgery and my answer to the Chief's question brought the reply: " Previously you have answered very well but now you are quoting Rose and Carless ". Each man was expected to reason to the best of his ability on his knowledge of anatomy and physiology and to arrive if possible at a rational diagnosis. That might not be the correct one as proved later at operation, but if it was arrived at honestly and the reasons for it were valid, that student got greater credit than the one who had made an intuitive or " spot " diagnosis, even if it proved correct.

The above was the routine on Tuesdays, Thursdays and Fridays between 9.15 and 11 a.m. From 11 a.m. till noon Sir William operated and had with him on the floor of the theatre the clinical clerks and the anæsthetic probationers. Any others who wished to attend went to the gallery. On Mondays the class met for instruction in bandaging and fractures. Here the students were divided into three sections of roughly thirty men and a lecture of forty-five minutes was given by the assistants to their respective groups. From 10 to 11 a.m. the students put up the fractures discussed that morning. They were questioned on the points brought out in the lecture and their practical work was corrected if necessary. Each man treated his neighbour as patient. Wednesday was devoted to operations, Sir William being in the theatre from 9.15 a.m. to 12 noon. Meanwhile the class, minus the senior clerks, was taken by the senior assistant, Dr J. A. C. Macewen, who devoted most of the time to instruction on surgical technique. A most helpful feature and one eagerly looked forward to by the men was the demonstration of specimens and casts on alternate Fridays. This took place in

the operative surgery classroom at the University
—a large tiled hall with glass roof. Casts of
actual cases, specimens and photographs bearing
on the work done at the hospital since the previous
demonstration were laid out on long tables.
Subjects of such demonstrations that come
readily to the mind are " groin swellings ",
" tumours of the breast ", " diseases of bone ".
If cases of hernia or of hydrocele had been under
discussion in the hospital wards there would be a
demonstration of specimens illustrating groin
swellings, including scrotal and testicular conditions with which they were liable to be confused,
while a scirrhus cancer of the breast would be
associated with the whole range of breast
affections. These demonstrations greatly assisted
the students to put cases they had seen in their
true perspective.

Another thing Macewen taught with
characteristic thoroughness was the adminis-
tration of anæsthetics. A short series of lectures
was given, followed by a written examination.
Those who passed had to act as anæsthetic
assistants at eight cases and on twelve subsequent
occasions were required to give the anæsthetic
under supervision. Then a certificate was issued
indicating what the student had done. No one
was compelled to take the course, but he would
have been a queer man who did not do so.
Chloroform was Macewen's anæsthetic of choice
and its action on the human body was discussed
fully in his lectures—particularly its effect on

the heart and respiration and on the pupil of the eye. The responsibility of the anæsthetist was impressed on every student. Macewen insisted that whoever was giving the anæsthetic, and in so doing taking away the consciousness of the patient, was in reality the patient's brain until he recovered consciousness. It was clearly understood that the anæsthetist must give undivided attention to his job and not interest himself in anything else.

In reviewing any subject Macewen taught us to take all related matters into consideration and to think clearly. In this way he helped us to be self-reliant and precise ; in all his teaching such was the aim of one of the most mentally alert men I have ever met. But there was no tension in the process. For Macewen was friend as well as counsellor and guide and a fine spirit of comradeship existed between teacher and student. This was in evidence almost every day at the Clinic. On the opening day of my first session at his class at the Western Infirmary I happened to be called as the junior to the floor. As I came forward Sir William said, " Stretch out your arm ". As I did so he measured his arm against mine and said, " I still have it "—thinking doubtless of his reach in fencing. On another occasion he was testing the grip of a patient and he gave the dynamometer to several of the students to press. I asked if I might try it. Being puzzled that the sparest man in the class should register the highest reading he asked to see my hands. " Ah, you must be accustomed to manual labour ". My hobby was poultry breeding and I told him I often wheeled heavy barrows.

Everyone shared in the camaraderie. A very happy New Zealand final year student sat near the middle of the back row of the benches to the right of the Chief. Early in the session he used to chat to the man on either side of him and yet follow the discussion on the floor. Several times Sir William asked him a question to see if he was listening but he always answered well. " You must have a special brain, Mr X, that enables you to converse with your neighbours and yet listen intelligently to me. But it is unlikely that all those around you have, so please allow them to concentrate on what we are saying on the floor ". Another day I remember well. The Chief asked me what happened in certain circumstances. I hesitated, finally replying, " It all depends ". He chuckled and said, " That is the correct answer. Now let us examine the alternatives ". And before the discussion was over every student in the class had to do some hard thinking, which left us in possession of knowledge which was to be part of us for the rest of our lives. That is real teaching and Macewen was master of the art.

Macewen's teaching was supplemented by practical demonstration whenever possible and he had a gift for evolving the simplest method of achieving results. Most of his students must

B

have seen him reduce a dislocation of the shoulder. The patient was laid flat on his back on the floor. The Chief stood on a stool and with his two hands took the affected arm just above the wrist. Then slowly and steadily he would lift the patient off the ground. In many cases, after a few minutes, the muscles of the arm would relax, when the Chief would give the arm a sudden slight sharp shake—almost like a handshake— and the head of the humerus would slip into position. With very muscular or very heavy men, and in cases where previous attempts at reduction had been made, an anæsthetic might prove necessary to induce relaxation of the muscles. This method is so simple and easily remembered that old students of Macewen must often have used it. I must confess I always give an anæsthetic. The patient is glad of it and so is the surgeon, for with the resulting complete relaxation of the muscles, the procedure is the simplest possible.

In all hospitals, nursing is a vital factor and no one knew better than Macewen what a surgeon owed to the nursing staff. He was very conscious of the help he received especially from those nurses, trained by himself, who sat by his brain cases in the pre-operative stage noting every detail by day and night. He knew it was they who provided the data that enabled him to decide where he was to go at the operation. At the opening of the Australasian Medical Conference in Melbourne in 1923, the gallery was occupied by nurses in uniform and Sir William, before giving his address, looked towards them and said how fitting their presence was in such a gathering and how much their co-operation meant to the medical profession. No surgeon has ever done more to raise the status of the nursing profession than Macewen.

As an operator he was deliberate and fearless rather than fast, but no operation was ever performed without the most painstaking investigation and careful differential diagnosis. For two years I was present at almost every operation he performed and although he was often confronted with difficulties, I never saw him at a loss. His technique was meticulous and he continued to use the carbolic method after others had given it up. With the use of carbolic Lister introduced antiseptic surgery; on this Macewen built, and in due course brought in the aseptic age. The methods adopted by him in those early days in the preparation of surgeons and patients for operation are of interest historically. The Chief and his assistants did not wear gloves except in septic cases. The hands and arms were washed in running water for five minutes by the clock, with nail brush and soft soap, particular attention being paid to the nails. The hands were then immersed for two minutes in one-to-twenty carbolic aqueous solution. Sterile gowns and sterile masks were worn. The steel instruments were boiled for twenty minutes. The catgut used was prepared by the sister-in-charge according to a method evolved by the Chief. The patient's skin—not only the part to be operated on but well beyond it—was washed with soft soap and water and then shaved. A turpentine swab was gently rubbed over the area to remove any fatty material and all traces of turpentine removed by free application of methylated spirit. Lint moistened in one-in-forty carbolic solution was applied to the part. This was done on two successive days and finally one hour before operation lint moistened in one-to-twenty carbolic was applied. The wearing of sterile gowns, the boiling of instruments and special preparation of catgut are now so much the order of the day that young surgeons will have difficulty in thinking of them as innovations, which they undoubtedly were when Macewen adopted them.

But although getting rid of germs in advance made surgery safer than before, Macewen stressed the fact that every operation was a potential danger to the patient and that every care must be taken to minimise that danger. The anæsthetist, we have seen, had to confine himself to his job. Further, nothing was allowed to interfere with the concentration of the operator ; no speaking was allowed in the theatre either on the floor or in the gallery. Even before the operation began speaking was prohibited, for Macewen used to say that if the patient heard something disturbing when losing consciousness he or she would be likely to come round from the

anæsthetic in a state of dread. Modern anæs-
thesia with rapid intravenous induction has got
over that difficulty, but silence could well be
invoked with advantage in many operating
theatres to-day.

One of the things he imparted to me as a
house-surgeon was that as much care should be
taken in the preparation and conduct of a minor
operation as of a major one. He himself paid
the greatest attention to every detail that might
improve his operating. He was most careful
about the design and temper of his steel instruments, and about the sterilisation of the catgut
prepared by his own chromic acid method, and
he was responsible for the design of his operating
table. But the factor that affected Macewen's
results most of all was the care of the patients
themselves. For example, patients who had to
undergo excision of the tongue were taught to
tolerate the passing of a stomach tube before
the operation ; and before the operation for
cleft palate, the palate and throat of the child
were regularly tickled with a feather to accustom
it to the irritation of the stitches. His courtesy
to hospital patients under examination by students
in circumstances very strange to them was at
times touching. One case is clear in my mind.
A Highlander, short in stature and some fifty
years of age, with epithelioma of the lower lip,
was brought into the teaching corridor with its
ninety students. He had been admitted to the
wards only the day before and had never

previously left the clachan where he was born,
as his accent showed. Macewen proceeded to
put him completely at his ease. In an easy and
somewhat hearty manner he asked the man his
name, where he lived and what he did for a living.
And I thought the students that morning were
to be commended for restraining their mirth.
He came from Kilchoan, and when asked where
that was, he said, " It is where Argyllshire and
Inverness-shire are disconnected ". For a living
he helped his brother and when asked what his
brother did he replied that he kept a cow and did
a bit of fishing. It was only after this friendly
contact that the surgical aspect was reviewed.

But Macewen was more than a successful
operator ; he was the acme of the scientific
surgeon. Back in the laboratory, he was tireless
in his approach to new problems and ceaseless
in his enquiry after truth. It was these faculties
that made him a pioneer in so many branches of
surgery. Even as a young police-surgeon the
scientific observer was at work. He made the
discovery that the pupil of the eye in a man
unconscious from alcoholic poisoning behaves
differently from the pupil in a man unconscious
from injury or disease. This proved a most
important point in medico-legal work and the
test was soon applied everywhere.

It is still not recognised in some quarters that
Macewen was the first surgeon successfully to
remove a lung, and that in an ordinary theatre,
in 1895. Only a few years ago, at a gathering

of surgeons, I had to point this out when a prominent senior surgeon had overlooked the fact in his paper on " The History of Lung Surgery ", but he quickly and generously made amends. It is not difficult to understand how such an error can occur when one finds in *The British Journal of Surgery* of July 1936 a paper on " Total Removal of a Lung " by R. Milnes Walker in which he states : " Though the operation was first attempted as long ago as 1910, no successful case was reported until 1931 ". Macewen, at the International Medical Congress held in London in 1913, reported on four cases of removal of a lung for tuberculous disease. The discrepancy is probably due to the fact that Mr Walker was thinking of pneumonectomy as practised to-day for bronchiectasis and cancer. Sauerbruch of Germany, in his autobiography, made a different kind of claim. His " 1905 pressure chamber ", he said, made thoracic surgery possible for the first time. Up till then, he claimed, " nobody had ever operated inside the fully opened thorax ".

How was it that Macewen dared to operate on the lung in an open theatre at a time when it was firmly held by all other surgeons that opening the chest meant immediate collapse of the lung ? Several factors were at work. In the first place he had always been interested in the possibility of a surgical approach to the lung and as far back as 1875 he had written on penetrating wounds of the thorax. The next step came when he attended an accident in which a man's chest was laid open, yet the lung had not collapsed, a fact of observation which was contrary to current belief. At this juncture it is certain that a period of further observation of chest wounds and a study of physical forces followed. Every student of Macewen can recall his experiments with a wet leather sucker attached to a string. If the sucker is pressed firmly against a smooth flat stone and the string lifted, the stone is raised attached to the sucker. That this is not due to atmospheric pressure was proved by hanging the contraption inside a bell-jar from which the air was removed. The stone remained attached to the sucker. He also showed us that two pieces of smooth wet glass pressed together could not be pulled apart. In the Cavendish Lecture of 1906 Macewen stated conclusions he had reached in the latter part of the previous century. "Experience shows", he said, "that the lung is maintained in full expansion by the molecular cohesion existing between the two surfaces of the pleura and the capillary attraction exerted by a thin layer of serous fluid existing between the two moist membranes ".

Macewen was now ready to operate in an open theatre when occasion demanded, and for that matter on a table that to-day would be considered utterly inadequate. The next step came from a senior colleague, Sir William Tennant Gairdner, a brilliant physician who had been President of the British Medical Association at the Annual General Meeting in Glasgow in 1888 at which Macewen had figured so prominently. For him Macewen had the highest regard. In 1895 Gairdner asked Macewen to take over from his medical wards a very serious case of unilateral tuberculosis of the lung. The physician was convinced that only surgery could save the patient's life. The successful removal of this man's tuberculous left lung was the first operation of its kind in the world. I remember the man well, for it was my duty, over a period of time, to examine him at intervals. He lived to a ripe old age after a life of normal activity— at least once using the remaining lung unwisely. Walking home one evening in Glasgow, Sir William thought he recognised a voice making public utterance to a street audience. There was his patient in the centre of a Salvation Army gathering discoursing in a loud voice. The Chief waited until he had finished and then told him that open-air preaching was something he could not safely indulge in !

The hold surgery of the lung had on Macewen's mind can be gauged by the fact that the last surgical address he ever gave was on this subject—at the Australasian Medical Conference in Melbourne in 1923. It was a great thrill to us old students resident in Australia to hear him once again on this favourite topic.

Almost greater were Macewen's achievements in the realm of the central nervous system. He was the first man to operate on the brain following localisation of the seat of the disorder deduced from physical signs. That was in 1879 in a case of subdural hæmorrhage. Later in the same year he removed a tumour from the brain, and he would have evacuated a brain abscess in 1876 had the parents of the child not refused operation on the advice of a second consultant. A post-mortem examination proved Macewen to have been correct, but few in those days believed an operation possible. Even thirty years later I remember my apprehension when I first saw the Chief evacuate pus from the brain.

In the years I was with him he operated on brain cases, mostly tumours, from all over the world, but never without the most exhaustive search for and investigation of physical signs. The interpretation of these signs determined the area to be attacked. Before my time the Chief removed the whole left half of the cerebrum of a young woman because of a very extensive tumour. Yet, back at work after her operation, she retained the finer faculties that physiologists said were solely the function of the left half of the brain.

There was a high degree of sureness about Macewen's brain work. His summing up after investigation of the physical signs was so complete and clear that one felt he would go straight to the affected area and find what he expected. But he was always aware of the difficulties of brain surgery and every case was approached with meticulous care. He wrote much on the surgery of the central nervous system and three of his contributions deserve special mention. " Pyogenic Infectious Diseases of the Brain and Spinal Cord ", published in 1893, is a classic that no student of the subject can afford to ignore. It is a finished work. His " Atlas of Head Sections ", published in the same year, is a monument to the intensive study he made of the brain and evidence of the energy with which he applied himself in everything he did. The other contribution to which I wish to refer is the address he gave on " The Surgery of the Brain and Spinal Cord ", at the Annual Meeting of the British Medical Association in Glasgow in 1888. By then he had operated with success on twenty-one cerebral cases and six cases of elevation of the posterior laminæ of the vertebræ.

His work on the brain has received such prominence that his operations on the spinal column have been overshadowed. But they are equally worthy of note. One case taken from this address will suffice. In 1884 a girl was brought to him in what appeared to be a hopeless condition and it was only her pathetic and urgent appeal that induced him to act. The lower part of her body was devoid of sensation, the limbs were cold and livid, she could not move and she had no control over the intestinal and urinary functions. On cutting down on the spinal column and removing several of the posterior bony plates a dense connective tissue tumour was found between the bone and the theca. The spinal cord at this

level had shrunk to half its width and looked like
" an inanimate rod ". Ten hours after the
tumour was removed the limbs had lost their
lividity and they were warm to the touch. From
the fourth day she regained control of the bodily
functions, and while sensation returned quickly,
it was six months before she could move her
limbs freely. In eight months she could walk,
attend to herself, and help in the house. From
then on she enjoyed life again.

Macewen's bone work was no less outstanding
than his brain and lung surgery : in many ways
it was revolutionary. Until Macewen proved
otherwise, everybody believed that bone grew
from periosteum. He showed, however, that
bone was reproduced only from bone cells or
oestoblasts and that the periosteum was merely
a limiting membrane of fibrous tissue. It took
the profession many years to admit this.
Macewen applied this new principle in his
surgical practice. I remember well a man from
whom, in youth, he had removed the diseased
shaft of the humerus—dead bone due to oesteo-
myelitis—and in the gutter had planted small
fragments of healthy bone. The man grew a
useful arm and, after training by Macewen, he
became the attendant in charge of the University
surgical laboratory. Eadie became a very
efficient technician in all laboratory work,
including photography. I saw much of him
in 1910 and 1911 when I used to prepare
the Chief's bone sections and report on them

histologically. The day came when a visiting Australian surgeon offered him a position in Sydney which, after consultation with the Chief, he accepted.

No less dramatic was the case of a Highland officer wounded in the South African war. His leg was so badly damaged that the military surgeons deemed amputation necessary, but the patient refused permission. He was sent home and eventually consulted Macewen. The man was overwhelmed when he found Macewen confident the leg could be saved. The operation was completely successful and the man able to live a life of great activity for the rest of his days.

Even more spectacular were two cases of repair of the lower jaw. The more complicated one is described in detail by Macewen in " The Growth of Bone ". A girl of fifteen had a very misshapen face, from which her upper teeth stuck out prominently. She could not chew her food and there was constant dribbling of saliva. She had had half her lower jaw removed some years earlier for disease and this was the result. But until she was taken to Macewen it was considered nothing could be done. I doubt if Macewen ever faced a more difficult problem, but by very careful dissection of the skin of the lower jaw and the insertion of bone taken from one of her ribs a notable operative success was obtained. Some years later, with no visible scar, beauty had returned to her face, a dental plate resting on the newly made lower jaw enabled her to chew, she could speak well and was happy.

In this book Macewen writes of a second similar case, which, "though of less extent and presenting fewer difficulties, was likewise operated on with good result ". I believe this is the case he described to me between operations one day in 1910. A lady who entertained a great deal had to have one half of her lower jaw removed because of a tumour and naturally a disfigured face was anathema to her. Sir William agreed to remake the jaw, promising not to use bone from an animal. The patient in her turn promised to ask no questions until the surgeon's work was completed. Unknown to the mother, her daughter was admitted to the nursing home and, under an anæsthetic, bone was removed from a rib. This piece of bone was put in a saline bath and the mother immediately operated on. An incision being made in the skin immediately behind where the jawbone would eventually be, bone from the daughter's rib was placed in the gutter thus formed and the skin closed. When the lady was ready to go home she asked what bone had been used, at which point the Chief left mother and daughter alone. This lady entertained freely after this—the scar behind the jaw unnoticed by her guests.

In early days fractures of the patella were notoriously hard to heal and no one seemed to know why. One day Macewen witnessed an unusual accident in which the knee-cap was broken by muscular action. On examination, he found that the fibrous covering of the bone had got between the upper and lower fragments. Here was the cause of failure to heal—fibrous tissue keeping the bone cells apart. From then on in such cases Macewen removed the torn fibrous tissue and wired the broken ends of bone together. Healing followed without delay.

The treatment of talipes or club foot was another matter in which Macewen broke with tradition. We were hardly ever without these cases in the wards. It had been the custom for others to cut the soft tissues in the hope of rectifying the deformity, but Macewen satisfied himself by investigation that the fault causing the deformity was in the bones. In every case he tackled the bones, with different treatment for different cases.

A hundred years ago ricketts was very prevalent in Glasgow as in all great industrial cities. Macewen was not the pioneer here, but it was he who devised the operation which became universally adopted. It was worked out only after the most careful investigation of the bony deformity and by experimentation. The deftness with which he used scalpel, osteotome and mallet, and finally his hands, in the breaking and straightening of these deformed bones was thrilling. But such confidence and dexterity were the result of earlier days of thought and labour when he was still in his twenties. The osteotome was his own invention, finalised only after a careful assessment of requirements and after he was satisfied that no form of chisel could safely make the required cut in the bone. Hosts of men and women have walked erect in Glasgow, saved by Macewen in their childhood from bow-leg and knock-knee. Soon, with better housing, better food, more fresh air and sunshine and more exercise in early life, ricketts will be no more. It has already almost disappeared.

A disease which implicates bone—chronic inflammation of the middle-ear—was common in the days before penicillin and the sulpha drugs. Surgical interference was necessary, not only to get rid of infection from the ear, but also to prevent thrombosis of the sigmoid sinus and a possible brain abscess. A radical mastoid is a most delicate operation and calls for an exact knowledge of local anatomy. Few realise the long and painstaking research Macewen made of the skull in the region of the ear. He made a minute study of the cavities of the middle-ear and their relation to the brain, the venous sinus, and the bony canal which protects the facial nerve. It was he who found the safest way to the diseased area through what is now known as " Macewen's triangle " and it was he who introduced the gentlest method of penetrating the bone—by means of a rotating burr and his own type of gouge. He made an investigation, too, into the clinical history of middle-ear disease which led him to condemn the common habit of syringing a discharging ear. I saw him do many radical mastoids, one of which, where he had to operate on both sides, being burnt into my memory. The patient was an adult woman, one of many patients on whom the Chief had operated at the Western Infirmary just before the Christmas vacation in 1909. On his final visit for the year he was still giving me helpful advice as I walked with him in the dusk to the Dumbarton Road gate of the Infirmary. As his tramcar approached he turned sharply. " I am leaving you a heavy responsibility but I know everything will be all right. A happy Christmas ". What an uplift to a man who had graduated only six months before! And this was but a foretaste of the encouragement I was to receive from time to time. The patient with the double mastoid was very ill and two nights later became delirious but she made a good recovery.

Early in the century tuberculosis was a very common disease in Scotland and some forms called for surgical interference. In Macewen's wards at the Western Infirmary at that time there were many cases of tuberculosis of the bones and joints, some cases with the disease in the middle-ear, in glands of the neck, the mesenteric glands of the abdomen and other parts of the body. Whatever the part affected, Macewen put total treatment of the patient first—rest of the body and rest of the affected part, insistence on fresh air, sunlight, nourishing food and cod liver oil if it did not upset the digestion. Nothing was allowed to interfere with digestion. Bovine tuberculosis was so common then that Macewen had a strong preference for goat's milk. One wonders whether goats will retain their immunity to tuberculosis. They are now being housed and fed intensively; they get less natural foraging and the stress is on greater and greater milk production.

Among more specific forms of treatment, my notes of Macewen's lectures mention Koch's old tuberculin, with a word on Wright's " opsonic index ", Bier's passive congestion, Bipp paste and Finsen light. This shows that Macewen made use of and introduced his students to every new move in the fight against tuberculosis.

The Chief treated each case on its merits— there were variations with almost every patient —but to indicate the principles on which he worked only those types that were most frequently in the wards will be discussed.

Tuberculosis of the spine was very common, and its most frequent manifestation fifty years ago was psoas abscess—a tuberculous or " cold " abscess due to tuberculous disintegration of vertebræ in the dorso-lumbar area. In all cases of psoas abscess, the general treatment referred to above was at once put into operation. In the very early stage it was often difficult to distinguish the condition from early tuberculous disease of the hip-joint. Macewen's differential diagnosis between the two illustrates his genius for simple but effective tests based on pathological inter-ference with normal function. In early cases the spine was rested in a position of extension until nearly straight, then a plaster-of-Paris jacket reaching from the axillæ down over the pelvis was applied over a stockinette singlet which was changed as required. The spine was thus kept at rest and there was hope of cure for such a case after a year or two.

A late case of psoas abscess bulging in the groin was in a different category. The Chief stressed the fact that tuberculous " pus " did not contain pyogenic germs but that if these were allowed to gain access to a tuberculous cavity they would run riot and might endanger the life of an already debilitated patient. He also pointed out that tuberculous pus was shut off from the surrounding tissues by a membrane of two layers, the inner of which may swarm with tubercle bacilli, while the outer layer was protective. Two guiding principles were evolved from those considerations—the protective layer had to be maintained at all costs and pyogenic germs had to be kept out if at all possible. Macewen did not open the abscess at once but, under strict asepsis, injected iodoform once a week, the puncture in the skin being sealed with collodion. If the swelling became tense, he withdrew some of the pus with the syringe before injecting more iodoform. Sometimes these measures did not stay the progress of the disease. In that case Macewen radically exposed the whole track of the abscess, wiped away with gauze the infected inner layer of the wall and left intact the outer protective layer. The track was then lightly packed with iodoform gauze or the surfaces dabbed with Bipp paste and the wound stitched.

Macewen had a high regard for the French surgeons of his day and I have often wondered whether their orthopædic work stimulated his mind in relation to methods of spinal extension, the general use of plaster, and the value of iodoform. Calot in his book on " Indispensable Orthopædics " states that it was in the laboratory of his Chief, Professor Robin, that the action of iodoform was worked out. Iodoform did not act as an antiseptic, but was found, he said, to provoke an outpouring of white blood corpuscles which were later destroyed. This set free ferments, one of which attacked the fatty envelope of the tubercle bacillus while another destroyed the body of the bacillus itself. Every time I have read Calot's work I have had the Chief in mind. My feeling is that there was very probably an interchange of ideas between the two schools.

Tuberculous disease of the joints was perhaps the commonest manifestation of tuberculosis in the surgical wards. Macewen showed that the disease actually started in the bone—in the growing end of a long bone—and from there spread to the joint. The knee, the hip and the elbow were the joints most commonly affected and in that order. Children and adolescents were most often affected.

If a case was detected while the disease was

confined to the epiphysis, Macewen excised the focus to prevent spread to the joint. Rarely, however, was a case seen before the joint was swollen and then treatment consisted of general health measures—rest of the affected limb in extension, injections of iodoform and Bier's passive congestion. On improvement, the joint was fixed in plaster of Paris.

In advanced cases, with much ulceration of cartilage, excision of the joint became necessary. In excision of the knee-joint a fixed result was the objective, but in all the other joints movement was aimed at and Macewen was particularly successful in achieving this. To ensure this result he took the greatest care to do as little damage as possible to the tendons and joint capsule consistent with the thorough removal of all diseased parts—articular surfaces, bone, synovial membrane and everything else affected. In these cases the ends of the bones were left narrow and passive movement of the new joint was begun early and repeated at regular intervals. Surgical treatment of tuberculosis calls for un-remitting care and infinite patience as well as specialised knowledge. Macewen had all three in a marked degree.

Hernia is another ailment which Macewen treated differently from his predecessors. There were two cardinal features in his operation. He felt it was essential to get rid of the depression in the parietal peritoneum at the internal ring. To do this he brought the puckered-up hernial sac to lie over this funnel-like depression so that it acted as a " break-water " to divert the peristaltic waves of the intestines and helped to spread abdominal strain. It was also essential, he insisted, to shut off the inguinal canal from the abdomen by a stout layer of musculo-aponeurosis. This he did by bringing down the arch of the conjoined tendon by means of mattress sutures and fixing it behind Poupart's ligament. This operation, conceived before 1880, became the basis of future planning for the radical cure of hernia. His results were excellent, partly due, I think, to the post-operative rest he prescribed.

Macewen was greatly interested in the treatment of aneurysms. Where it could be performed, he used the ligation method of Hunter—tying the artery some distance above the aneurysm—but it was in the large aneurysms of the aorta that he was chiefly interested. Prior to his method of dealing with them, the aim had been to produce ordinary red blood clot. But this soon contracted, and it was friable, so the possibility of fatal embolism was very real. Macewen, in his investigations, came to the conclusion that only white thrombi (those formed mainly by the deposition of platelets) could offer any prospect of closure of the aneurysm. Macewen convinced himself by observation and experiment that, where the interior of a blood vessel had been damaged, white thrombi formed. By what means, then, could he induce the formation of white thrombi in the larger aneurysms of the

aorta ? He decided on scratching of the inner
wall of the aneurysm by means of a specially-
made, highly polished steel needle. This was
pushed in till it just touched the opposite wall of
the sac. Sometimes the heart-beat was able to
move the needle sufficiently to do the scratching,
sometimes the Chief used his hand. The point
of the needle was shifted from one place to
another, and in half-an-hour or so a good bit of
the vessel wall was covered. The operation
demanded the utmost concentration, and
Macewen stood over the patient all the time. I
can recall him at work on such a case ; it was a
thrilling experience. The thrombus which formed
was firm ; it gradually increased and ultimately
was organised into fibrous tissue. The modern
surgery of aortic aneurysms was not envisaged
in those days.

Cases of appendicitis were always present in
the wards. The type coming for operation to a
general hospital in the first decade of the century
differed greatly from the cases seen to-day.
One did see simple acute cases and some in the
quiescent state between attacks, but the majority
were admitted only after they had become
seriously ill. Not only the appendix but the
neighbouring large bowel might be acutely
inflamed. Sometimes there would be dense
adhesions, sometimes an abscess, and not in-
frequently a ruptured gangrenous appendix.
Such cases still crop up but they are now the
exception. In the simple acute and interim cases

the Chief closed the wound and applied a narrow strip of gauze permeated with collodion. In the severe toxic and abscess cases he left the wound open, inserted a single layer of gauze along the walls and bottom of the wound and packed the sac thus formed with sterile gauze swabs. These were changed as required but the single layer of gauze was removed only after protective granulation tissue had formed. The cavity would then heal by granulation from the bottom up. That was the technique while I was a student fifty years ago but very soon thereafter it was replaced by the removal of the appendix with the first attack and the operation became a simple one. Macewen was greatly interested in the function of the appendix and was of the opinion that research might prove that it played a part in digestion taking place in the large intestine.

The feature of Macewen's abdominal surgery that left its deepest imprint on me was the care he took in arriving at a diagnosis before operating. At first the abdomen as a whole was considered ; then, according to the signs of the case, he would concentrate on one of the four quadrants and try to assess what was happening there. If the case permitted, he would review the whole matter the following day. At that time X-rays were in their infancy, Barium meals had not been invented, and isotopes were beyond our ken. But despite the mechanical aids available to-day, personal clinical evaluation of symptoms and signs is still of first importance. Delicate handling of stomach and intestines is another "fundamental" which Macewen impressed on his students.

Macewen was one of few surgeons at the latter end of the nineteenth century who believed that a patient suffering from cancer could be cured. He was convinced it was at first a local disease and if detected early could be eliminated by operation. He was, too, one of a small band who insisted that all lymphatics and glands in any way connected with the tumour should be removed with it in one mass and without the tumour being cut into.

The commonest form of carcinoma seen in the wards was that of the breast, and Macewen's method of dealing with it may be taken as an indication of his treatment of cancer elsewhere. His incisions went well beyond the growth to include what was believed to be healthy skin. The muscles between the tumour and the ribs—pectoralis major and minor—and their fasciæ were removed, and all fat, lymphatics and glands in the axilla. Everything was removed in one mass and the tumour was never cut into until it had been detached from the body.

Charles Moore of the Middlesex Hospital, London, was at the age of thirty the originator of the modern operation for cancer of the breast. That was in 1866, and in 1886 Macewen was one of the very few who recognised the merit of his work and built on it. Macewen took the stand that every sufferer should be given the chance of recovery, unless, of course, there was secondary involvement of vital tissues. This implied his belief that many of the early cases and even some late ones of the chronic scirrhus type could be eradicated. Macewen recognised, of course, that some types were so malignant that no guarantee could be given, however thorough the operation.

Macewen was a general surgeon and operated on all types of cases, but I have mentioned only those operations in which I feel he played a distinctive part. His hatred of mutilation of any kind and his perseverance in the face of difficulties impressed me greatly. No surgeon ever took greater pains to conserve tissue, and the amputation of a limb was never performed except for the saving of life. Many years later I was called to a man who, in a motor accident, had sustained a severe compound comminuted fracture of both bones of the leg. At the end of seven weeks there was no union of the bones. I then plated the tibia but after another six weeks there was still no union and practically no callus showing in the X-rays. Amputation was advised but I would not agree. There was a constitutional element in this case and following the exhibition of five grains of thyroid extract three times a day great outpouring of callus took place. When he visited Adelaide the Chief was very interested to see this man and his X-rays. After the removal of the plate, the young man resumed soccer football for many seasons.

The clinical teaching and the operating at

the Western Infirmary were only part of Macewen's work as Regius Professor of Surgery. The systematic lectures in general and regional surgery were given at the University during the winter months, and the lectures in operative surgery and the practical operative work in the summer session. The systematic lectures began with a detailed description of the process of repair in the healing of simple wounds, and the causes and results of inflammation. In this way the value of asepsis and the avoidance of infection were ever before Macewen's students in the University and hospital alike. Only after that were we introduced to the disorders of the various tissues and to the surgical treatment of the different organs of the body. Macewen always held the attention of the class. As a lecturer he was alert in manner, clear in enunciation and forceful in expression. To a notable degree he had the gift of easing the strain of intensive listening by interposing an entertaining interlude. For instance, speaking on the importance of keen observation he suddenly asked : " In the stillness of the night when you are studying do you ever watch the little mouse that comes out in search of crumbs that may have fallen from your supper-table ? Scratch the knife on the plate and watch him jump ! " A smile was now on every face and the momentary relaxation enabled us to listen again with renewed concentration.

Preparation for the operative class was very thorough. Each student had to learn the steps of the operation he was about to perform and to pass an oral examination before being allowed to proceed to operate on the cadaver. And the students were questioned by the Chief and his assistants while they were at work. Macewen's work as surgeon and teacher may be summed up in words I used in my appreciation at his passing : " One word describes everything he did— thorough ".

Once when I was house-surgeon I asked the Chief why he did not write a manual on surgery. " Well, you see, I am not a good collaborator. I should have to write the book myself and before it was finished the first part would be out of date." There was nothing static about Macewen's surgery.

At the British Medical Association's Annual Meeting in Glasgow in 1954 a surgeon of authority said in my presence he was glad he had not studied under Macewen. I asked his reason and he replied, " He failed to found a school around him ". I wish to answer that criticism. What was the position in Glasgow when Macewen was Regius Professor of Surgery at the University ? He had three wards in the Western Infirmary but only in virtue of his University appointment. He had three University assistants but the authorities at the Western Infirmary did not accept them as members of the staff of the Infirmary. The result was that when Macewen was in residence in the city he had to do all the operating himself, emergencies as well as planned cases. None of his University assistants could act for him on " receiving " days. Macewen in this way was grossly overworked. If he was out of town on a " receiving " day, the superintendent sent another surgeon of the hospital to see newly admitted cases requiring attention. At all other times, in the Chief's absence, the house-surgeon was responsible for the patients in the three wards—unless he cared to ask the superintendent for another surgeon of the hospital, which I never did. Later, as a University assistant of Macewen, I had no official status at the Western Infirmary and could not take responsibility of any kind. It is not difficult to understand why his assistants could not put up for long with such an intolerable state of affairs. No school was founded by him because no group of keen young surgeons could be held together under the conditions to which Macewen and they had to submit. But if such a school did not form around Macewen, what of the host of men he trained and who practised surgery according to his methods, both in Glasgow and all over the world ?

It would be impossible to overestimate the benefit gained by students from the thorough training and the example of Macewen. Four days after graduation I was able, through the Macewen method of pressure on the abdominal aorta, to save a woman's life from hæmorrhage. My first operation in Australia, in a home in a small country township with no hospital, was a

mastoid which I should have had difficulty in
tackling but for the landmarks and steps the
Chief had taught us and shown us again and
again. The worst hare-lip and cleft palate I ever
encountered I was able to repair from notes I
had taken of his cases when the textbooks I
consulted proved of little help. The result was
excellent and when the case was shown at a
British Medical Association meeting I was asked
to describe the steps taken to achieve it. Here
was the Macewen influence again.

I have always been grateful to a medical
relative who advised me to go straight from
anatomy and physiology to Macewen's surgical
clinic at the Western Infirmary. Macewen, he
said, was teaching a new outlook on surgery and
he insisted I should learn it from the start. There
were ninety-two students in that summer session
at the Western but only two from my year. On
the first morning Dr J. A. C. Macewen handed
us slips of paper on which we had to write our
names and state how much clinical surgery we
had already done. Before the Chief arrived the
numbers were arranged according to seniority
of study. Then the Chief took over. " Two
men, I see, have had no previous experience of
surgery. Will they please stand." We did so,
and then, with a student of each of the two years
ahead of me, I was called to the floor. My
ignorance of surgery was complete ; I had never
before seen varicose veins and of course could not
name the condition. But I could describe what I

saw and was able from my knowledge of physiology and anatomy to give certain conditions
which could cause dilated veins of the leg. At
the end of the discussion Sir William advised me
to sit on the front seat and to pay as much attention to the cases as if I was on the floor. That
summer in surgery was mental stimulation from
first to last.

In the next five years I was to see much of
Macewen in many capacities, and as a result to
know and appreciate him as a man. He had a
natural dignity, but he was very friendly; he was
a man of candour, but I never found him unkind ;
he had a passion for truth which made him
intolerant of insincerity. Very few, however,
realised he was a sensitive man. That he did not
show his wounds did not mean that he had not
been wounded. Once I saw him suffer deeply
and most unfairly, but the public saw only the
erect figure as before. Before I went to the
Western Infirmary as house-surgeon an older
doctor told me I would not last a term with
Macewen. According to him the Chief insisted
on implicit obedience and my independent spirit,
he said, would not suit him at all. Nothing could
have been further from the truth. I was loyal
to the Chief at all times and I worked hard for
him, but he could hardly have had a house-
surgeon or an assistant who differed from him
more.

We were in opposite camps in politics. In
Glasgow in 1910 Sir William was one of the

Conservatives' most influential chairmen while I was speaking for the Liberals several times a week. He asked me how I justified my attitude, and, politely if a little nervously, I gave my reasons. Later, when it was stated that I would probably be a candidate at the next election he was most interested, but I assured him I had no intention of leaving medicine. In religion too at that time we did not see things in quite the same light. The training of my home in strict Sunday observance led me once to ask Sir William to allow me to stand down from an outing on the Clyde. I was almost taken aback by the tenderness and consideration shown me. Even in the surgical sphere I did not follow slavishly. On a Sunday evening when the Chief was at his country home an emergency arose in a case of gangrenous ruptured appendix operated on by the Chief a day or two before. The man was highly toxic and had become unconscious. I took a new line of action which in the circumstances I judged to be the right one. At the bedside on his return the Chief asked why I had done this and on hearing my reason he remarked with interest, "We must watch this". The man recovered with two days out of his reckoning. That was invariably Macewen's reaction if one could give an adequate reason for any departure from routine treatment, but haphazard alteration of technique met with disapproval and rightly so. Sir William was always ready to discuss and to try out a new method.

It is not generally known that the Macewen department at the Western Infirmary included out-patients, who were treated in a room off the main corridor that led to the wards. Here one saw the type of patient that forms such a large part of general practice. Cases with a needle in the hand or a chip of metal in the arm were very common and one soon realised how difficult it sometimes was to find the foreign body. I devised a method that helped greatly. Two thin straight steel rods or knitting needles were fixed so that the antero-posterior and the lateral aspects of say the arm were divided into halves. The arm was then screened in the X-ray room and it was simple to fix the position of the metal or needle in each plane. From that one got the actual position of the foreign body. As house-surgeon I had removed many offending fragments in this way. In the wards was a young woman with part of a needle deep in her buttock. In spite of an X-ray film the Chief could not locate the needle, for an X-ray on one plane only is of little value beyond demonstrating the presence of the needle. I asked if I might try my method. " What is your method ? " the Chief asked, and after I had explained it he said, " Certainly let us try it but wait a few days till the patient gets over the anæsthetic ". The Chief allowed me to do the operation. I had marked the skin on the two planes—the needle was very deep in the fleshy buttock. I had cut down and down without coming on the needle fragment. The Chief was

D

retracting the wound and very graciously did not interfere. Hopefully I said, " It is deeper still ". At the next cut the knife struck steel and with a tremendous sense of relief I held out my left hand for long forceps. I mention these two cases to show how false is the impression that Macewen ruled those under him with a rod of iron.

Macewen was a scrupulously honest surgeon. I never knew him take credit for what was not his due. In 1910 his wards in the Western Infirmary were visited by Fellows of the American College of Surgeons. One evening, some time before their visit, I phoned Sir William to come to the hospital to operate on a boy with acute osteomyelitis of the upper end of the right femur. His temperature was 105° and he was unconscious. " Have a look at the case again," he said, " and make quite sure it is not the lower end—that is the usual place isn't it ? " " Yes, sir, but it is the upper end this time," I said. The boy was on the operating table when the Chief arrived. He first cut down on the lower end and got a show of thick dark altered bone marrow. He looked at me. " Please cut down on the upper end, sir ". With a clean knife he did and up came a flow of pus. This boy was one of the cases demonstrated to the American surgeons and one of them remarked, " This is a rare case, did you diagnose the upper end at once ? " " No," said Macewen, stepping aside. " My house-surgeon did ". Not all distinguished surgeons are so generous.

As an examiner he was essentially fair, and
of this two examples will suffice. The external
examiner in the Final oral examination handed
a student a narrow cylindrical black vulcanised
object and asked what it was. A long pause
brought the further question, " What does it
look like ? " The lad still hesitated, and at
last remarked, " It looks almost like a fountain
pen, sir ". The examiner laughed. Sir William
took the article and remarked, " It reminds me of
a fountain pen more than anything I can think
of—what is it ? " " Why ", said the examiner,
who was not a Scot, " surely a trocar and
canula ". " But surely ", said Macewen, " you
don't call that a surgical instrument in these
days ? " The other incident concerned an able
student who knew his work but from sheer
nervousness was answering stupidly. In
Macewen's wards it was the custom to call men
for the oral while they were doing the practical
fracture examination, and during this period
the Sister of the wards gave each student a cup
of tea and dainty scones. Sir William was
examining and, after getting several stupid
answers, he asked the lad, " Did Sister give
you a cup of tea ? " " Yes, sir," came the
hurried, nervous reply. " Well I think you had
better have another cup of tea and another
scone ". The poor fellow was abject when he
came out and I had hard work to assure him the
Chief was giving him a chance to settle his
nerves. When he was called later he had regained

his balance and had no difficulty in satisfying the examiners.

I have heard Macewen described as a man of severity, one who brooked no divergence from his views—a man difficult to get on with. Never at any time was that my experience, but it is easy to understand why this view has gained credence. Macewen was at least fifty years ahead of his time; his ideas acclaimed to-day were revolutionary then and to many of his fellows quite unacceptable. He was a pioneer, and the pioneer is nearly always decried. It was Lister's fate before Macewen and it has been the fate of others since. He expected loyalty and whole-hearted effort from those under him but when these were forthcoming he increased one's responsibilities all the time.

No keen student of surgery, whatever his age or country, ever sought his advice in vain. It has been said that he was sparing in the giving of testimonials. The truth is that he gave testimonials only in the terms in which he felt they were merited, both as to professional ability and personality, and they carried no meaningless excesses. I hope I merited the one he gave me ; I certainly cherish it highly as I do his words to me on my last day as senior house-surgeon. He said he could not recall one occasion on which I had unnecessarily sent for him to operate, and he expressed his appreciation. The Chief was quick to sense another's mood and was very wise if his advice was needed. " You look worried,"

was how he hailed me one morning, and I told
him I had just received an insulting letter from a
lawyer. "You'll answer that I have no doubt",
he said, "but don't be in a hurry. If drafting
a reply later in the day will make you feel better
do it by all means but do not post it. Put it in a
drawer and the next day you will write a better
letter, but put that also in your drawer. In a day
or two you will write a satisfactory reply, but
until then do not commit your letter to the post."
No better advice could have been given to a
spirited youth.

Sir William had a gift for quick repartee. A
doctor from New York had arranged to see him
operate at the Western Infirmary at 10 a.m.
the following morning. At five minutes to ten
the Chief was still in his room when the visitor
arrived. He seemed upset and to Sir William's
"Good morning," replied "You said you would
operate at ten this morning". "And so we
shall." "But it is now five minutes to ten and
in my country we have a bath before we operate."
"Ah," came the immediate sally, "in my
country we have a bath whether we operate
or not!"

Soon after my appointment to the University staff I was staying for the week-end at
Garrochty, Sir William's country home. At
afternoon tea Lady Macewen said to me, "Now
that you are going back to Sir William I
hope you will do your best to see that he comes
home from the University at a reasonable hour

of night ". But the Chief had heard the remark
and with a merry twinkle in his eye said to his
wife, " Duguid is my assistant—nothing more ".
Lady Macewen was referring to Sir William's
habit of returning to the University after dinner
to continue his researches in the surgical
laboratory and staying long after he should
have been in bed—and he walked both ways.
This incident, one of the happiest possible, I
told in my obituary appreciation of the Chief
in the *Medical Journal of Australia* and I
added, " He always held the reins ". This
sentence has evidently been completely mis-
understood and I was amazed to find the story
used by a writer in support of his statement that
Macewen was a hard taskmaster to all who worked
under him. To me the word " taskmaster "
applied to Macewen has no meaning at all. In
his care of nurses he was outstanding and his
treatment of young medical men working with
him in my time could not have been more con-
siderate. Holding the reins does not imply
cracking the whip ; it means directing the team
and that was Macewen's duty at the University
and in his wards. His sense of responsibility
in these two spheres was a great example to
those of us who, in his absence, were sometimes
left in charge.

Sir William's surgical building was demo-
lished in 1954. It consisted chiefly of a large hall
full of light because of the amount of glass in its
structure. In this hall the students did their

practical operative surgery and it was here the surgical demonstrations were given once a fortnight. Through a door on the south side of the building one entered the main research laboratory and off this was the Chief's inner room where he worked alone.

As the newly appointed third assistant I was given only a small section of the class to begin with. In those days I was well acquainted with the requirements of the students in anatomy, physiology and surgery and I had time on my hands. Nine of them took high places in the examinations at the end of the course and in the next year too many enrolled in my section. Attention was drawn to this and the Chief, with a smile, shot me the question, " Did you institute a canvass during the vacation ? " The numbers were adjusted but Sir William asked me to come to the wards at 8.30 a.m. to conduct tutorials on the cases he had dealt with the day before.

Apart from his work I would say that Sir William's chief interests were agriculture and the sea, with grand opera in the winter months. He revelled in the parties he took to the opera and he remembered his senior nurses and house-surgeons. Some of his old assistants, now Chiefs themselves, were present on almost every occasion. Nearly every week-end, apart from the war years, he spent at Garrochty. There, with the help of his youngest daughter, who was a trained expert on dairying, he interested himself in milk production from Toggenburg milch goats which were being imported about that time from Switzerland. Sir William bred a herd and carried out research on the immunity of goats to tuberculosis. Garrochty had its own seaboard and the Chief was never happier than when sailing on the waters of the Firth of Clyde. But during the war years he had little leisure and the constant heavy work left its mark. He was Surgeon-General in Scotland of the Royal Navy, with the rank of Rear-Admiral, and he never spared himself. Sir William, however, possessed the greatest of all assets—the love and devotion of his wife and family. In his home he enjoyed complete relaxation and from it he went out refreshed.

Macewen was physically a very fit man, very cheerful, and never to the end showed the slightest stoop. Over six feet in height, he was a commanding figure in any company. I can see him now, standing on the pier at Kilchattan Bay—it was 1910. As the steamer drew in a lady standing immediately behind me remarked to her husband : " I'm sure that tall, erect man is a retired General ". When in Melbourne in 1923 he was taken to see the race for the Melbourne Cup, but what interested him most that day was not the race but the great number of men on the course who were taller than himself. At the Australian Medical Congress he worked far too hard, and that following a strenuous tour of the United States of America. I told him

when he came to Adelaide I was going to see he
went to bed early every night. He smiled
benevolently.

Adelaide, however, very properly wished to
entertain Sir William in a manner fitting to
the President of the International Society of
Surgery, and he was anxious to see as much
as possible of the surgical work and life of
Adelaide. There were two dinners in his
honour—one at Government House and one
given by the British Medical Association to
enable the members of the medical profession of
South Australia to meet him and to hear him
speak. For the rest of the week he had dinner at
home and he had some free mornings. These
he spent examining the various eucalypts and
the citrus and other fruit trees in the garden. He
was anxious to find out why some of the
lemon trees have spines. On one occasion I
came home to pick him up for a luncheon in
town. No one knew where he was but in the end
he was found sitting on a carpet of pine needles,
his back against a large fir tree, writing a letter
home.

In those days we had three acres of grass-
land behind the garden where we kept a cow
and bred turkeys and fowls. At dinner one
night I asked the Chief if he would have turkey
—it was a tremendous gobbler. He looked at
it and turning to his son said, " Willie, observe
an Australian turkey ". Every night I had a
hot bath ready for him at 9.30. There was one

incident over this. Sir William was in conversation with a lady and I waited a few minutes before telling him his bath was ready. A little later I had to remind him that the bath would be getting cold. " Has the position between us altered ? " he asked as he turned to me. " It has for this week, I'm afraid, sir ", I replied, and with that the Chief rose smiling and went to bed.

The relaxation of a home was probably of some value, for he worked as hard as ever when he went to Western Australia, even descending to the depths of a Kalgoorlie gold mine. There was one very hot day during his stay in Adelaide and my wife arranged for us all to go to the coolness of the beach, taking a picnic meal for the evening. The day the Chief left us for Perth was another scorcher, the temperature well over the hundred with the sun beating fiercely from a cloudless sky. At the railway station the medical profession of Adelaide turned out in force to say farewell to the distinguished surgeon who had come to Australia to represent the British Medical Association of the homeland. Everyone felt that the six hours' journey in a crowded train before Sir William and his son would join the modern Commonwealth Transcontinental express at Port Augusta would be a very trying experience, and so it proved. As the train started moving Sir William caught my hand, " You must come home again in the next year or two ".

His death soon after his return was a great shock. He had given himself freely wherever he went and he represented the British Medical Association with dignity and distinction. At seventy-five he was still young in spirit ; he had led a life full of activity and it was perhaps fitting, as one looks back, that the end came while he was still in harness.

It will be a long time before Glasgow knows another of the calibre of Macewen.

PRINTED IN GREAT BRITAIN BY
OLIVER AND BOYD LTD.
EDINBURGH